My Body

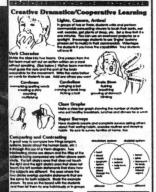

What better topic for a whole language theme unit than the human body! Kids are fascinated with their bodies and the many functions they have. Now is a great time to introduce your students to some of the body's internal systems such as the skeletal, digestive, central nervous and circulatory. And a whole language approach to teaching is fascinating too because it provides opportunities for experiences in all areas of communication and in all areas of the curriculum.

So have a total body experience with a great unit that incorporates oral and written language, reading, poetry, vocabulary development, math, social studies, science, art, music . . . the list is endless! The unit culminates with *A Better Body Bash* to be shared with parents or another class. How long you spend on the unit will depend upon how much you extend the activities and the capabilities of your class. Enjoy!

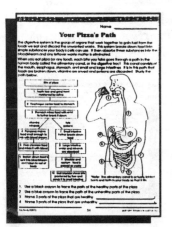

Teacher Resource Pages

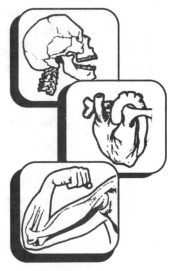

120 Reward Seals

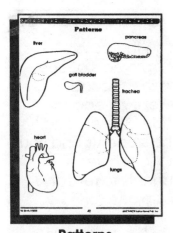

Student Activity Pages

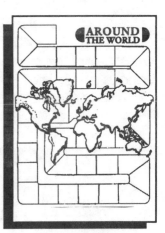

A Full Color Gameboard

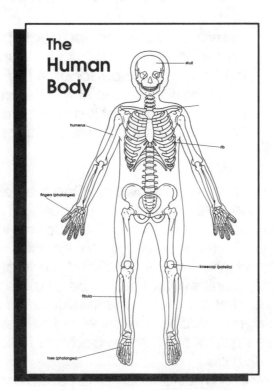

A 6-foot Black and White Banner Which Reflects the Theme!

Patterns

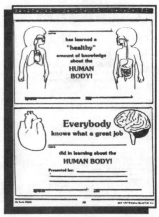

Award Certificates

1

Setting the Stage

When you begin your **My Body** unit, decorate the entryway into your classroom so it reflects the human body theme. Pull out the banner in the back of the book and tape it together so that a skeleton is formed. (You may want to make several copies of the skeleton to use with other activities.) Hang the skeleton near the doorway. Then, cut out, color and tape the body part patterns from pages 40-42 around the skeleton. (You may want to enlarge them using an opaque projector.) This will pique students' curiosity as they arrive at school. Suggestion: Read all the way through the unit before you begin.

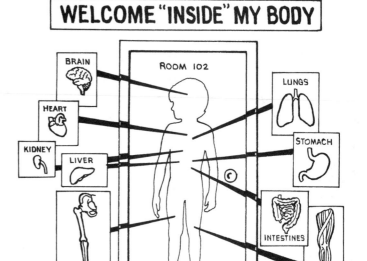

Using the Skeleton Banner

The skeleton banner can also serve as a wonderful teaching tool. For example, you can have students label all of the bones. (There are 206.) You can also use the body parts patterns (pages 40-42) to show students where they are located in the body. Another fun way to use the banner would be to laminate it, and you and the students could draw in the various systems of the body as they are discussed.

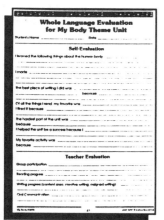

The Parent Connection

Make copies of the letter on page 39 to send home when you begin this unit. (Sign and date it first.) If you want to add anything to personalize the letter, just write it inside the simple heart. Parent involvement is a great way to improve parent communication.

Evaluation of Students' Work

The unit evaluation can be developed in two ways. One is by assessing on the basis of skills, knowledge, interest and behavior using the student projects as one criterion and observation of the students in class as the second criterion. These observations (anecdotal records) kept on each activity will give you information for a final evaluation. The second part of the unit evaluation will be completed by the students and you. At the end of the unit, guide the students through the *Whole Language Evaluation* on page 43 that asks the students to reflect on their study of the human body and allows you a place for evaluation also.

Hint - Make a master copy of an anecdotal record sheet. Write the students' names on it. Make several copies of this sheet. You will now be ready to make notes for each activity.

Creating the Environment

Setting up your classroom using the human body as your theme will help unite your class as a "cooperative learning family" even as they walk in the door. To help your classroom reflect the human body theme, make the *Interactive Bulletin Boards* on pages 4-5. Some of them you will want to prepare ahead of time, such as "System Success." Others you will want to set up as the unit progresses.

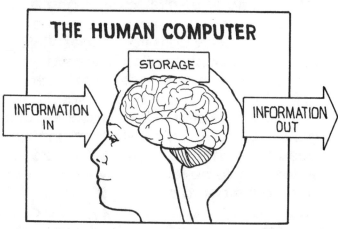

Another way to incorporate the human body theme into your classroom is with learning centers. Some suggestions for centers are given below, but more ideas for learning center activities can be found on pages 10 and 11.

To help your classroom further reflect the human body theme, use the seals in the back of the book on your classroom calendar where the date is added each day.

Math and Science Center

This area can be as simple as a table set up for use with hands-on math and science activities such as *"Me"asurements* (page 24.) Set the table near a bulletin board so you can incorporate a math or science interactive bulletin board into the center such as "Class Pulse Check" (page 5) or "Match Dem Bones" (page 4).

Creative Writing Center

Set up this area as a writing workshop as well as a place to display students' written work. Include all kinds of paper, *My Body Stationery* (page 45), markers, pencils, pens, cans of story starters, construction paper for book covers, stapler and tape. Page 14 has lots of fun writing ideas all students can enjoy and benefit from.

Reading Center

There is a wealth of books both fiction and nonfiction in your school library or public library about the human body. *Literature Selections* are given on page 46. Encourage students to bring any books from home, but be sure they are identified. Put class made books in the center. Include pillows so students can be comfortable. Read to your students often.

Interactive Bulletin Boards

System Success

Once students know they are going to be studying the human body, divide them into four groups. Assign each group one of the following systems - circulatory, digestive, central nervous and skeletal. Give the groups the body parts from pages 40-42 and any other aspects relating to the systems they have been assigned. Have each group research its system and prepare questions to post on the board for the other groups to answer. Have students answer the questions in their spare time. (A different system should be featured every day or each week.) The groups should attach the body parts to the board and any other pictures or items they feel are necessary for others to better understand the systems. (They could also show where the parts belong on the banner skeleton.) Before it is time for the next group to present its system, have the group whose system is featured give a report using the information it obtained. Each group should ask the other students questions, perhaps in game form, to see how much they learned.

Match Dem Bones

This is a great board for students to use to reinforce names of specific bones.

1. To make the border, cut 3" x 18" strips of paper.
2. Fold each strip in half and in half again.
3. Use the pattern to make bones that will unfold like paper dolls. Be sure not to cut on the folds!
4. Hang the skeleton banner or a skeleton from Halloween in the center.
5. Cut out the strips below and place them in a plastic bag. Hang the bag on the lower part of the board.
6. Fold a piece of construction paper in half. Glue a copy of the labeled skeleton on page 44 on construction paper and hang it next to the bag on the board with the answers hidden.
7. Students choose from the bag, find the bone that matches on the skeleton and hang the names of the bones with push pins. They can then check their answers.

clavicle	femur
humerus	patella
scapula	tibia
vertebrae	skull

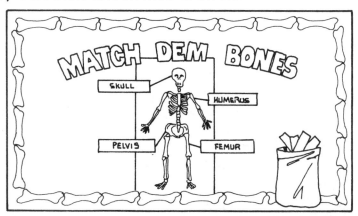

4

More Interactive Bulletin Boards

System Search

After studying each of the systems featured in this book, this bulletin board will serve as an excellent review!

1. Make the bones as explained on page 4 (Match Dem Bones).
2. Cut out four dog bowls and write: Skeleton Spike, Circulatory Snoopy, Digestive Dino and Nervous Neptune on each bowl. Cut slits 4" across in the center of each bowl.
3. Cut 16 bones from white paper and write one of these words on each:
   stomach, liver, esophagus, pancreas, joints, pelvis, clavicle, vertebrae, cerebrum, cerebellum, medulla, spinal cord, vein, artery, pulse, blood cell.
4. Place the bones in a paper lunch bag marked TREATS and hang it on the bottom half of the board.
5. Hang the four bowls on the board. Be sure to staple them about 3" below each slit!
6. Students choose bones and put them in the slits on the dog bowls in order to match them with the correct system.

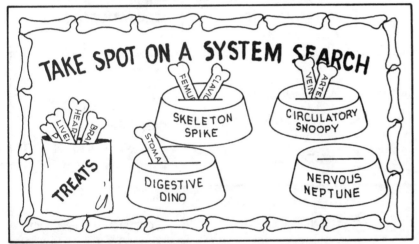

Class Pulse Check

Attach a large piece of newsprint to a bulletin board. At the top, write Class Pulse Check. Down the left side, write the numbers 50-150 in increments of 5 starting with 150 at the top. Draw a vertical line to the right of these numbers. Draw a line going across the bottom of the board about 3" from the bottom. Under this line, write actions like walking, jogging, jumping, sitting, standing, etc. Have students check their pulses for one minute after they do one of the actions. Find the group's average and plot it on the board. Do all of the activities for a couple of days. Be sure to note the time you have students do the activities. Each day you work with this board, use a different marker to see the differences in the group's pulses (i.e. students might be more or less active today maybe due to more or less sleep, food, etc., or it is earlier/later in the day than the other times you did the activities, etc.). You could also have students do the activities in pairs at a center during free time and plot them on individual graphs.

| 150 |
| 145 |
| 140 |
| 135 |
| 130 |
| 125 |
| 120 |
| 115 |
| 110 |
| 105 |
| 100 |
| 95 |
| 90 |
| 85 |
| 80 |
| 75 |
| 70 |
| 65 |
| 60 |
| 55 |
| 50 |

SITTING — AFTER WALKING — AFTER STANDING — AFTER JUMPING — AFTER LYING DOWN — AFTER JOGGING — AFTER RESTING

CLASS PULSE CHECK

Daily Journal Activities

Staple blank papers together and encourage the students to record their feelings through pictures, letters, words, etc. Below are some suggestions. Choose one a day and share it with the class in the morning.

Write one fact about your eyes and how to protect them.	Write a poem about your teeth. Include two facts.	List 5 bones and why they are important to you.	Write three ways to have a healthy heart.
Write why our veins are important.	Using illustrations, explain how arteries work.	Name a disease that can affect the lungs and one way to prevent the disease.	Draw what your kidneys look like and what they do.
List 10 foods that your stomach enjoys. Put a star by the ones that are good for you.	Draw what a liver looks like. Then, make it into an animal.	Write what would happen to your body if you had no esophagus.	Write a poem about the brain beginning each line with one of the letters in brain.
Write a story about someone with a spinal cord injury.	Write 3 facts about the large intestine.	Pretend you are explaining to a young child what a gall bladder is. Write what you would say.	Compare the small intestine to another organ of your choice.
Make as many 3-letter or more words as you can using the letters in pancreas.	Find an article in the newspaper about health. Glue it in your journal.	Make a wordsearch using some of your body's organs.	Draw your skeleton and label at least 5 bones. Write one way to have healthy bones.
Make a menu of foods that are bad for you.	Babies are born with 350 bones and adults have 206. Write a math problem using these numbers.	Write a short story pretending you are a hamburger. Tell what happens to you when you are eaten.	Design nutrition labels for a package of cookies and for a cup of yogurt.

Beginning the Unit

Now that you have worked so hard preparing your classroom, it is time to begin the unit! After your morning business is completed, gather the students and tell them you are beginning a new unit about the human body. Talk about the human body using the K-W-L graphic organizer below. Then, read to students the original story, *Bad Habit Harry* (page 8). After the story, show students the skeleton banner from the back of the book. See if they can point out where some of their organs are located. Then, discuss the importance of eating right. Have them name some foods which are good for them and have them tell which part(s) of the body the foods benefit.

Building Background Knowledge

A **K-W-L** graphic organizer helps students arrange their knowledge into 3 categories: What We **Know** About the Human Body, What We **Want** to Know About the Human Body, and What We **Learned** About the Human Body.

A clever **K-W-L** graphic organizer for this unit is to make 3 large silhouettes of body organs out of butcher paper. Use an opaque projector to enlarge 3 of the patterns shown on pages 40-42. First, make a copy and white out some of the detail so your lists will show up.

Encourage the students to brainstorm what they know about the human body and record their responses on the first organ. To stimulate their responses, lead a discussion by asking some of the following questions:

1. Can you name some of your body's organs?
2. Can you tell what these body parts do for you?
3. What are some of the systems in your body?
4. Which organs belong in these systems?
5. What are some ways to keep your body healthy?

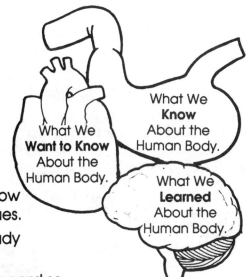

(Record all of their responses, even those you know are incorrect. A glossary on page 46 will help you keep some of the systems and some of their organs straight.)

On the second organ, record what the students want to know about the human body. Add to this list as the study continues.

The third silhouette will be used at the culmination of the study of the human body to record what the students learned.

Display the organs prominently in the room or on a bulletin board so the students can refer to them and add to them as the unit progresses.

Making a Big Book

Bad Habit Harry, the original story on page 8, can be reread and enjoyed throughout the unit by making it into a big book. Cut out the sentence strips on page 9.* Give two to each group, along with a large sheet of white paper.** (You may have to add more.) The students glue their strips to the bottom and illustrate them. Have each student make a healthy food item out of construction paper to glue on the cover for the book. If possible, make the cover out of tagboard to give it strength. As you compile the book, help the groups read their sentences and share the illustration.

*Make a copy and number the sentences to use as an answer key.

**Sequence the story as a group before you make the book.

Bad Habit Harry

An Original Story by Lisa Molengraft

"Harry! It's time to get up for school!" Harry opened his eyes and lifted his head from the pillow only to drop it again and catch a few more minutes of sleep. "Harry! You're going to be late!" His mother's voice was more stern as she flipped on his bedroom light and pulled the covers back. The chilly air forced Harry out of bed and into a pair of jeans and his favorite sweatshirt. He stumbled to the bathroom and brushed his teeth. On his way downstairs, Harry began to pick up pace as he grabbed a handful of cookies and ran out the kitchen door to catch the bus.

As he stared out the window, he was pleased to know it was Friday. This meant the day would include a spelling test and football tryouts. He wasn't terribly excited about the test as he'd had one of his raging stomach aches last night and couldn't study. Football tryouts, however, would be great! Harry was bigger than most of the guys, and his size alone should earn him a spot on the team.

The day progressed in the usual manner. Harry spent his lunch studying for the spelling test, which left him little time to eat. He quickly gobbled down some cake and milk, and then threw the rest of his lunch away.

Back in the classroom, Harry was trying to concentrate as Miss Lacey explained division with remainders, but he could not fight the fatigue and laid his head down on his desk. It seemed like seconds later that Miss Lacey was tapping his shoulder and Harry awoke to a room full of faces staring at him. He sank in his chair with embarrassment.

On his desk lay a blank spelling test. Harry listened to the words as Miss Lacey read them aloud, but he was too groggy to think and sloppily wrote the words on his paper. As he finished the test and turned it in, Harry was embarrassed again. He knew he'd done poorly on the test.

At last, the school day ended and Harry ran to the field behind the school for football tryouts. He noticed the other kids passing him as they ran toward Coach Dugan. Suddenly, Harry felt an incredible pain in his stomach that caused him to stop and double over, holding his mid-section. Coach Dugan ran to help Harry and sent him home immediately.

Harry's mother rushed him to the doctor as the pain had increased and her son was fighting tears. Dr. Ryan carefully checked Harry's stomach by pushing in different areas. Harry begged him to stop, but the doctor continued to search for the cause of the pain. At last, he asked what Harry had eaten the past two days. Harry explained that he'd eaten cookies for breakfast, cake for lunch and toast with jelly for dinner the night before. "And how much exercise have you gotten recently?" asked Doctor Ryan. "Well, I just got a new video game and I haven't been playing outside very much." Harry wondered what difference that made. "Am I dying, Dr. Ryan?"

"No, Harry, but you are very sick. You have made yourself sick by eating poorly and getting too little exercise. You have probably been more tired lately, too. That's because your body needs vitamins and minerals to stay healthy and energetic. There are several systems in your body, each with needs that you must give it by eating well, exercising and getting plenty of sleep. I have some medicine for you, but you can help yourself more by changing your habits."

As Harry's mother drove him home, he thought about Dr. Ryan's words and promised to think about the decisions he made for his body. He planned to talk to Coach Dugan about another tryout, but then he realized that he was already part of an important team - his body fitness team. Harry felt better already.

Bad Habit Harry Retold

Harry tried to catch a few more minutes of sleep.

Harry's mom turned on his bedroom light to try to wake him up.

A handful of cookies is what Harry ate for breakfast.

A spelling test and football try-outs awaited Harry at school.

During math, Harry fell asleep.

Harry was too tired to think during his spelling test.

Harry ran to the field for football try-outs.

An awful stomachache caused Harry to stop and double over.

Coach Dugan sent Harry home.

Harry's mom rushed him to the doctor.

Harry told Dr. Ryan that he had eaten cookies for breakfast and cake for lunch.

Because of a new video game he'd gotten, Harry hadn't been playing outside much lately.

Harry asked Dr. Ryan if he was dying.

Dr. Ryan told Harry that he had made himself sick by not eating properly and not exercising enough.

Harry was told that his body needs vitamins and minerals to keep it healthy and energetic.

Harry realized he needed to take better care of his body.

Directions for use found on page 7.

Learning Center Ideas

Estimation Station

Set up an area that has a small table, a poster labeled, "Estimation Station," a fish bowl or other container and slips of paper.

Under the poster, write one of the daily questions listed below or make up some of your own. When students visit the center, they write their name and estimate the answer to the question. At the end of each day, announce the answer and give the winner(s) a candy heart.

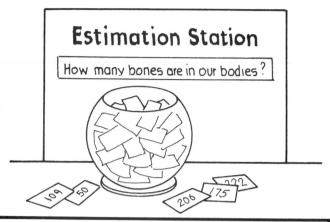

Daily Questions

1. How many muscles are in our bodies? *656*

2. How far around the world could your blood vessels stretch if laid end to end? *around the equator 2 1/2 times*

3. How many gallons of air do we breathe each day? *about 3,300*

4. Your skin grows new cells and eventually replaces itself. How often does this happen? *15 to 30 days*

5. What percent of your body is water? *65%*

6. How long in feet is your small intestine? *about 22 feet*

7. How many bones make up the skull of a human adult? *22*

8. How many pints of blood are in your body? *your weight x .08*

9. How much does your liver weigh? *about 3 pounds*

10. How fast do messages travel to your brain? *about 100 yards per second*

11. During your life, about how many pounds of food will your body digest? *about 60,000 pounds*

12. How many bones are in our bodies? *206*

Meeting at the Joint

To help students better understand bones and joints, provide the materials listed below for 7 stations and pass out page 22, *Meeting at the Joint*, to students.

*Provide items like a gallon jug, a ruler, a globe, a pint jar, weights, etc. for students to use.

Don't Be Chicken

After dinner, save and clean all the bones from a whole chicken. You could even bleach them. Place the bones in a plastic bag that seals and set out for the children to piece together. Provide the picture of the skeleton as an answer sheet.

*Also, in order for students to complete page 21, *Bone Up on Your Bones!*, you will need to obtain soup bones from a butcher. (Shin bones are ideal.) Have the butcher saw the bones in half.

More Learning Center Ideas

Operation!

Place the game Operation in a center for students to play when the noise won't disturb others.

Do Your Genes Fit?

Have students bring in one picture of themselves and one of their parents. Put all students' pictures in one envelope and all parent pictures in another. Students try to match parents with their children by observing their appearance. Before sending the pictures home, students hold the pictures of their parents and reveal the matches!

*You could also have students complete page 28, *Ingenious Genes*.

Our Super Senses

This is a great way to get students in touch with their senses and help them learn about the nervous system. Students will need page 32, *Our Super Senses*. You will need to provide the following materials to each group:

- 1 paper bag marked #1 containing a carrot stick, cracker, lettuce and apple slice
- 1 paper bag marked #2 containing celery, cereal, toast and raw spaghetti
- 3 envelopes marked #1 containing cinnamon, onion powder and chili powder
- 3 envelopes marked #2 containing pepper, brown sugar and flour
- plain gelatin made with 1/4 cup sugar (Color 1/2 yellow and 1/2 red.)
- mashed fruit and sliced pieces of the same fruit (can be mashed easily in a blender)
- small amounts of sugar, lemon juice, salt and cocoa
- small hand mirrors optional for touching parts of the tongue
- 2 plates
- 2 spoons
- 2 glasses of water
- 4 cotton swabs

A parent volunteer who would help prepare these things ahead of time would be wonderful! If not, perhaps you could assign each child to bring one of the ingredients listed.

Hearing
Sight
Smell
Taste
Touch

Skeleton Success

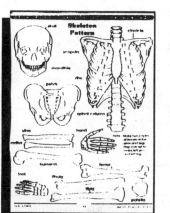

Provide students with a copy of a skeleton (perhaps the one from the book) and with copies of the organs on pages 40-42. Students can group the organs according to systems and place them on the skeleton. Or, you could provide clues like, "I am located in your chest. I am part of the circulatory system. I pump blood. What am I?" (heart) Students could use the clues to place the organs where they belong. Once the organs are in place, have them write poems about the organs and how they work together.

Developing Reading Skills

Language Arts

Reading aloud to students is important no matter what their grade level. Reading two or three times a day is not too often. When you read, make certain that your voice carries. Read with expression so the children feel like a part of the story. Before reading, let the children predict what the story will be about or share what they already know about the subject. This will activate their prior knowledge. This is also a strategy they should use before they begin reading a book themselves.

The children do not need to respond to every book that is read to them or that they read. What better way to kill the pleasure of reading for fun. Opportunities, however, are needed for children to discuss, write and listen to others' interpretations of a story. Allow time for discussion but use follow-up assignments with circumspect. The activities suggested on this page and on page 13 will not only get the children to read and write more, but will also get them to think and focus on the elements of the story. There are no right or wrong answers, but the children will respond the way they react to the writer's words.

Free Choice

At an assigned time (or when all work is complete), have students select a book from the Reading Center to look at and/or read. You may want to keep track of the books students select for their independent reading. If so, hold a conference with each student when he/she finishes a book. Fill in the form below (or a similar one, designed for the needs of your group).

Independent (Free Choice) Reading Record for _____	
Title _____ **Level** _____ **# Pages** _____	
Date Started _____ Date Finished _____ Conference Date _____	
SKILLS:	**Anecdotal Comments**
Ability to Select Book	
Word Attack	
Comprehension	
Oral Reading	
Enjoyment	
Genre	

☐ NF   ☐ Fantasy   ☐ Mystery   ☐ Humor   ☐ Poetry   ☐ Biography

Developing Reading Skills continued

Big Books

Big books are intended to be repetitious and patterned. Read *The Sandwich That Max Made.* Discuss the pattern of the book and brainstorm verses that could be added. Then, in pairs, students can use similar patterns to write a big book about the human body. For example,

page 1   This is your body with many systems.

page 2   These are the teeth that chew the food
that travels through your body with many systems.

page 3   This is the esophagus that's like a canal
From the teeth that chew the food
that travels through your body with many systems.

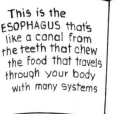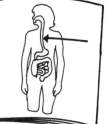

This is the ESOPHAGUS that's like a canal from the teeth that chew the food that travels through your body with many systems

You could have students make big books using any of the books listed on page 46.

Book Talks

One way for students to share books with classmates is through the use of book talks. In a book talk, the student shares the title and author, tells something about the book, shares a favorite picture and reads a page to the class. Then, three or more classmates and the teacher ask questions to the child sharing the book. Examples of questions to be asked are:

- If you could be a character in this book, which one would you be and why?
- Why was the setting important to the story?
- Why did you choose this book?

Book Activities

- Draw the setting, main character, or event.
- Make a time line of a story .
- List 3 facts about the main character.
- Describe the setting in detail.
- Write what the main idea of the story was.
- Look for words with the same spelling pattern (oa, st, ate, etc.).
- Do a research paper related to the book.
- Find words on specific pages that fit a visual pattern.
- Write the story's problems and tell how it (they) was solved.
- Find and write 3 good feeling sentences from the story.
- Write about how the story made you feel.
- Compare the book with other books by the same author.

System Express

Read either *The Polar Express* by Chris Van Allsburg or *The Magic School Bus Through the Human Body* by Joanna Cole. Have students imagine a train or bus that takes you through the human body. Ask them what they would see. Ask who would be on the train or bus with them. Have students write a detailed story about their journeys. They could also draw a map showing the route of the train or bus. Have them include a compass rose, map key and symbols.

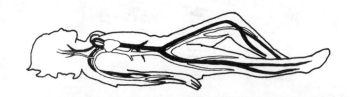

Creative Writing Ideas

MY SKELETON, MY TEETH ARE USED TO BITE AND CHEW. FOOD BEFORE IT GOES INTO MY DIGESTIVE SYSTEM. AS PART OF MY

Concrete Stories

This type of story is fun for students because it is written to form the shape of an object. Students draw the outline in black crayon, cover it with white paper, and follow the shape as they write. Then, a title and details are added. (See example shown.) Other ideas: heart, eye, outline of body, hand, foot, brain, bone, lungs

Body Dictionaries

In the back of their journals, students can use four pages to make their own dictionaries. They can label the left side of each of the pages with four letters alphabetically. Then, they should add three new words each day and write an explanation and/or draw an illustration for each word.

Funny Bones

Using the skeleton banner, pick out a funny-looking bone. Find out its real name, but then give it a new name - one relating to its shape. Explain your name.

A Heart of Gold

This expression is used to describe an unselfish person always willing to help others. Make a special card for someone who has a "heart of gold." Include a poem about him/her on the card.

Rewriting

Rewrite and illustrate *Bad Habit Harry,* but with one major change - Harry is a shaggy, overweight dog! Now he won't be trying out for football, but what could Harry the dog be doing? What happens to make him change his bad habits?

Good Habit Harry

Write another chapter to *Bad Habit Harry* in which Harry makes some changes. Is it hard for him to change? Does he stick with it? Does his life change?

Body Basics

Have students collect the Health, Life and Food sections of the newspaper. They should study how the articles are written and what pictures and captions appear with them. Students should search for articles relating to the unit. You can read some of the headlines aloud and discuss the content. Then, have students design a newspaper page and write an article about a new cure for a disease, diet tips, exercise information, etc. They should include pictures, captions and headlines.

Language Arts

Mystery Box

To make a mystery box, cover a box with wrapping paper and cut a hole 6" in diameter near the bottom and center of one side. Put different objects inside. Then, staple or glue an old sock over the hole. Children will slip their hands in the sock and then into the box without seeing what is inside. Provide "guessing paper" for the students to use to record their thoughts and describe what they feel. This is also a great way to practice adjectives.

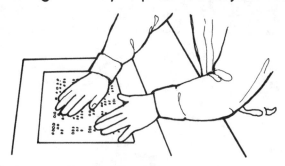

Braille

Discuss the use of the Braille system to help blind people read. Provide students with straight pins to use to write Braille messages. (See an encyclopedia for a copy of the system.) Have students exchange messages to let another classmate "read" the message with his/her fingertips.

Dream Log Book

As you study the central nervous system, ask students to keep a log book or journal next to their beds at night. When they wake up, have them write in the books or journals any dreams they remember. Discuss the possible thoughts that could have caused these dreams.

Be a Healthy Consumer!

Have students bring in two labels from their favorite foods to school. Make sure their labels give nutritional information. Then, using the information to the right, have students compare the two foods. Students can answer questions like:

1. How many servings of product A do you eat?

2. Which product has more protein to keep your body strong?

3. Which food is more healthy? How do you know this?

4. What foods could you eat to help your body get more protein? vitamin C? calcium?

5. What are the ingredients in the product? Which ones are you unfamiliar with?

| Product Name _____ |
| Serving Size _____ |
| Calories _____ |
| Protein _____ |
| Carbohydrates _____ |
| Fat _____ |
| Sodium _____ |
| Vitamin A _____ % |
| Vitamin C _____ % |
| Calcium _____ % |
| Iron _____ % |
| Riboflavin _____ % |
| Other _____ |

Poetry

Poetry Corner

Poetry is an exciting way to tell a story. Listening to poetry, reading poetry and writing poetry are keys to helping children gain an appreciation for it. Set up a Poetry Corner. Make it an inviting, comfortable place. Place a tape recorder in it so children can both record and listen to poems. Include a collection of poetry books. Display class poetry on the wall with the caption: **CLASS POETS**

Acrostic Poems

Acrostic poems are fun to write. Here is a step-by-step approach to get children writing.

- Write BONES down the chalkboard.
- Brainstorm words that begin with each letter and list them.
- Brainstorm sample lines for each letter.
- Put some lines together to make a poem.
- Have students choose a human body noun to write a poem about. Have them illustrate their poems.

B	- big, bad, bulky, beautiful
O	- obvious, oh, outrageous
N	- narrow, nice, noise, neat
E	- each every, even, Earth
S	- so, such, simple, success

Big, beautiful, bountiful bones
Oh! If you hurt them - such outrageous groans!
Narrow or wide bones - they all are so neat!
Each and every person has bones in his/her feet.
So be sweet to your bones and be sure to eat.

Shape Poems

A shape poem is written as a picture of the subject the poem is about. Write couplets on the board together using body nouns. Then, have students write their own 2-line poem around the shape of its subject. Suggest they do 2 or 3 of them. Display them with the caption: **CLASS POETS**

Haiku Poetry

Haiku poetry is originally from the country of Japan. It is a simple form of poetry and can or cannot rhyme. A haiku poem has three lines with a syllable pattern of 5-7-5. Often, it is about nature. Write some together and then have students write and illustrate their own. Either display them in the Poetry Corner or make them into a class book.

It works so hard to
Pump blood
   throughout your
   body.
The wonderful heart

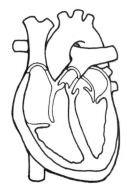

Creative Dramatics/Cooperative Learning

Lights, Camera, Action!

In groups of two or three, students write and perform commercials persuading viewers to brush their teeth, eat well, exercise, get plenty of sleep, etc. Set a time limit (i.e. one minute). You can use an overhead projector as a spotlight. Encourage students to use "jingles" (catchy phrases set to music) in their commercials. Videotape the students if you have the capabilities. Your students will love it!

Verb Charades

Divide the class into two teams. One person from the first team must act out an action written on a card without speaking. (See below.) His/her team members must guess the verb and the part of the brain responsible for the movement. Write the verbs below on cards for students to use. Add any others you want.

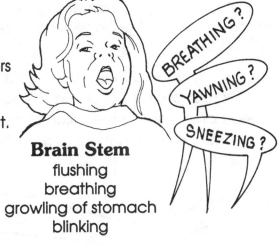

Cerebrum	Cerebellum	Brain Stem
memorizing spelling words	swinging a bat	flushing
creating a story	carrying a book bag	breathing
counting	kicking a ball	growling of stomach
multiplying		blinking

Class Graphs

Make a class bar graph showing the number of students who eat healthy breakfasts, lunches and dinners for a week.

Super Surveys

Have students create and complete surveys asking others about their eating habits, exercise routines and sleeping habits. Be sure to survey families at home, too.

Comparing and Contrasting

A great way to compare two things (organs, systems, books about the human body, etc.) is through the use of a Venn diagram. Two interlocking circles are drawn and the titles of the subjects being compared are written above each circle. The left circle's area that does not touch the right and the right circle's area that does not touch the left contain statements that show how the subjects are different. The area where the two circles overlap contains statements that are the same for both subjects. Study the example shown. Try one on the board with the students and then let them try one individually or in groups.

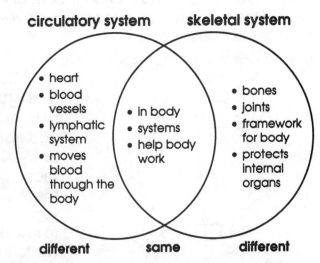

Oral Language and Music

Dry Bones

Try to obtain the instrumental version of the song, "Dry Bones." Below is a list of the bones as they are connected according to the song. Students can make up new beginnings and endings to the song to make it relate to their class. You can also do several activities with this song. Assign groups of students to make the bones. Then, as the students sing the song, the student(s) with the correct bone stands up next to the student with the bone it is connected to. When disconnecting the bones, the student with the bone called for sits down.

Another activity would be to have students point to the bones called for in the song on a skeleton. They could label the bones. Students could also find the scientific names for the bones and make up a whole new song using these names.

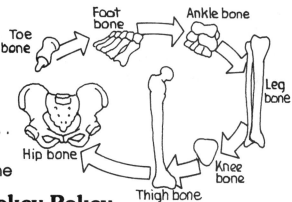

> your toe bone connected to your foot bone,
> your foot bone connected to your ankle bone, . . .
> leg bone, knee bone, thigh bone, hip bone,
> backbone, shoulder bone, neck bone, head bone

Hokey Pokey

Gather your class in a circle and sing the song, "Hokey Pokey," but substitute parts of the body going in and out. For example: You put your clavicle in, you put your clavicle out, You put your clavicle in and you shake it all about . . .

Harry Took a Bite of Food!

Students can make up songs about the digestive system or other systems using familiar tunes. For example, the tune of "Mary Had a Little Lamb" could be used for:

Harry took a bite of food, bite of food, bite of food. Harry took a bite of food that traveled through his body.

It went down his esophagus, . . . etc.

Harry took a bite of food

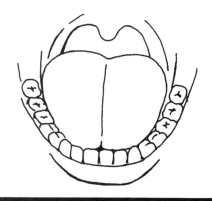

Tongue Twisters

Write a tongue twister on the chalkboard as an example: **Bad Habit Harry had a horribly hard time having a healthy body!** Then, as a warm-up, have students call out as many words as they can that begin with the letter H. With these words, create two or three new H tongue twisters together and let students take turns reading them. As a follow-up activity, let students create their own tongue twisters relating to the human body.

18

Games

My Body Lies Over the Ocean

For this game, you will need a large map of the world. Each student picks a country and they all sing "My Bonnie Lies Over the Ocean" using body instead of "Bonnie." Then, a student gets up and points to the continent on which his/her "body" lies. The student can give the other students hints about which country his/her body is located in. The class can also ask the student questions to try to figure out the country but they cannot directly ask which country it is. The student to correctly guess the country gets to go next and they all sing the song again.

Candy - 2		
Meat - 2	Fruit - 2	
Soda 0	Bread 2	Pie 0
Doughnuts - 2		
Vegetables - 1	Milk - 1	

Nutrition Toss

Copy the diagram to the left on pavement with chalk or on the floor with tape. Make it at least six feet long. Put another line three feet in front of it. Students stand at the line and toss five beans or pebbles, one at a time, onto the diagram. The area where they land tells students the number of points they score. The first player to reach 20 points is the winner.

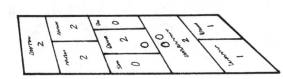

Guess and Go! Yes or No!

You begin by writing a secret body word on a slip of paper. The students ask only yes or no questions to try to figure out the secret word. If the same question is asked twice, do not repeat the answer. Students must be listening! The person to guess the word gets to write one and answer students' questions. For fun, keep track of the number of questions it takes to get each word. See if the class can improve that number by asking general questions and then narrowing them down to be more specific.

Rubber Bones

The skeleton is a framework of 206 bones that has three main jobs: to hold your body up, to protect your inner organs, and to produce new blood cells inside the bones. That means our bones must be healthy. The outer part of our bones is made of calcium, which keeps our bones strong. What would happen if the calcium became weak? Try the experiment below with a partner to find out.

Materials Needed
a chicken bone
a glass jar with a lid
1 cup vinegar

Procedure
1. Clean the chicken bone.
2. Place the bone in the jar and cover it with vinegar.
3. Cover tightly.
4. Let it sit for two weeks.

After two weeks:

How has the chicken bone changed? _____

_____

What would happen to your body without calcium? _____

_____

Rickets is a disease caused by too little calcium in your body, For this reason, calcium is found in many of the foods we eat. Check the labels of several foods. List at least ten that contain calcium.

1. _____
2. _____
3. _____
4. _____
5. _____
6. _____
7. _____
8. _____
9. _____
10. _____

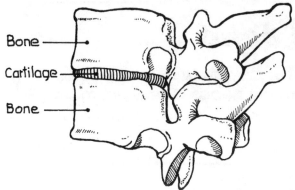

Bone ——

Cartilage ——

Bone ——

Bone Up on Your Bones!

When you were born, your skeleton was made of soft bones called cartilage. As you grew, most of that cartilage turned into bone. However, all people still have some cartilage in their bodies. Our noses and our ears are cartilage, and there are pads of cartilage between sections of our backbone that act as cushions.

Besides supporting the body, the bones also serve other important purposes. They are storage houses for important minerals like calcium and phosphorous and the center of the bone, called bone marrow, produces new blood cells for our bodies.

Try the experiment below to discover more about bones.

Materials Needed
soup bones from a butcher
(Shin bones are ideal. Have
him/her saw it in half for you.)

1. Look at the end of the whole bone.
    Find the parts labeled on the diagram
    to the right.

2. Now, separate the bone. Look inside the
    cavity which is filled with marrow. Write
    5 adjectives to describe the marrow.

    _____

    _____

3. Pull away the skin covering the bone.
    What is the name for this outer skin?

    _____

    If the bone is fresh, you will see small red
    dots where blood vessels enter the bone.
    Name two types of blood vessels.

    _____

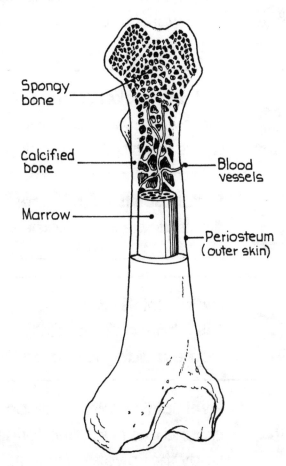

Spongy bone

Calcified bone

Marrow

Blood vessels

Periosteum (outer skin)

4. Carefully scoop out the bone marrow. Your teacher will now boil the bone to get it really clean. What do you see now? Write three facts about bones.

    _____

    _____

    _____

Meeting at the Joint

The many places where bones meet are called joints. They allow us to bend our arms, legs, fingers, twist our wrists and waists, and turn our heads. There are many types of joints that allow us to move. Visit the station around your room that your teacher has set up. Then, answer the questions below.

1 **No Joints!** - Try to walk without bending your legs. Write your name without bending your fingers. _____ What other things would be hard to do with no joints? _____

2 **Hinge Joints** - Open and close your classroom door. Watch the hinges. They work like a fold in a piece of paper. Name a part of your body that moves like a hinge. _____

3 **Ball and Socket Joints** - Put a ball inside a cup and roll it around, but don't remove it. Some of our joints work like this. Name a part of your body that works like a ball and socket. _____

4 **Saddle Joints** - Rub pieces of paper together. They move back and forth, like a saddle joint. Name a part of your body that moves back and forth. _____

5 **Sliding Joints** - Bend the zipper and move the train in curving patterns. This is how a sliding joint works with several bones bending together. Name a sliding joint area. _____

6 **Pivot Joints** - Spin the globe. This is how pivot joints work. They move around in a back and forth manner. Can you think of an area of your body that pivots? Name it. _____

7 **Fixed Joints** - Look at two pieces of paper that are glued together. They don't move or slide. Some bones in our bodies are fixed and don't move. Name one. _____

Skeletons in Your Closet

The expression, "skeletons in your closet," is used to refer to any secret you may have about yourself. Have you ever shared a secret? Have you ever been asked to keep a secret? Who did you tell? Did they keep your secret? Write about a time that you told or kept a secret. Then, place your writing behind a closet door. To do this, follow the directions below.

1. Write your story on the lined paper to the right. Cut it out.

2. In the center of a piece of construction paper that is larger than the lined paper, trace around the lined paper.

3. Starting in 1/2" from the traced lines, cut the right side and the top and bottom lines.

4. Fold the paper back on the left side to create a closet door. Glue the story behind the open door.

5. Decorate the closet door with a knob, posters, clothes, etc.

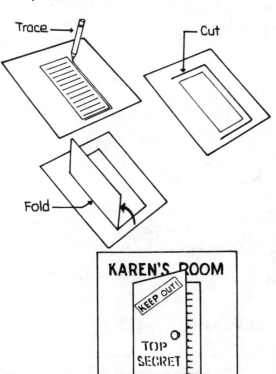

KAREN'S ROOM
KEEP OUT!
TOP SECRET

Name _____

Take Some "Me"asurements

Materials Needed

1 meter stick
1 piece of string 2 meters long
   or a tape measure
*At times you'll need a partner.

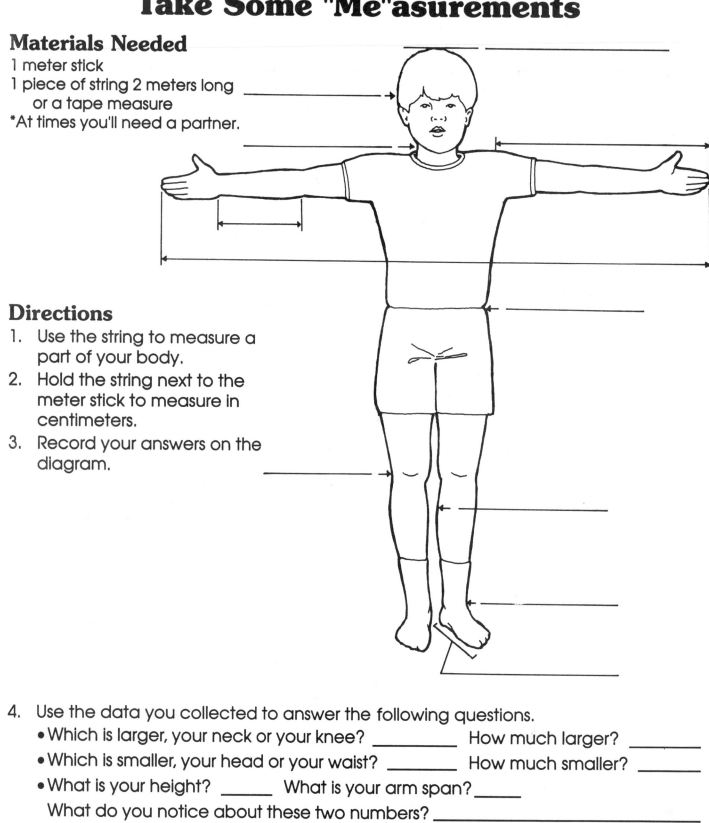

Directions

1. Use the string to measure a part of your body.
2. Hold the string next to the meter stick to measure in centimeters.
3. Record your answers on the diagram.

4. Use the data you collected to answer the following questions.
   • Which is larger, your neck or your knee? _____ How much larger? _____
   • Which is smaller, your head or your waist? _____ How much smaller? _____
   • What is your height? _____ What is your arm span? _____
     What do you notice about these two numbers? _____
   • What is the length of your foot? _____ What is the length of your forearm?
     _____ What do you notice about these two numbers? _____

We're Going Around in Circles!

The circulatory system is responsible for moving blood throughout your body. It is blood that carries food and oxygen to your body's cells and carries away carbon dioxide and other wastes. This system also carries disease-fighting substances that help prevent you from getting sick.

The main components of your body's circulatory system are: the heart, blood vessels, blood and lymphatic system. It is the heart, however, that controls this system.

The heart is responsible for sending blood mixed with oxygen to the rest of your body through arteries which are a kind of blood vessel. Your veins look blue because the blood in them has no oxygen. Back toward the heart, the blood gathers more oxygen as it passes through your lungs and becomes red. This cycle occurs about one time every minute. It is your heart's constant pumping that keeps your blood circulating.

Use the information above to solve the puzzle.

Across

2. The _____ controls the circulatory system.
4. Blood without oxygen is _____ .
6. Arteries carry blood mixed with _____ from the heart to the rest of your body.
7. _____ carry blood to the heart.

Down

1. _____ carry blood away from the heart.
3. Blood is _____ when it contains oxygen.
5. Blood gets oxygen from our lungs.

I Can Feel My Heartbeat

Each time your heart pumps the blood through veins and arteries, you can feel it! It's called a pulse. You can feel your pulse in two places where the arteries are close to your skin. Gently, place two fingers on the inside of your wrist or on your neck next to your windpipe. Silently count the pulses and complete the chart below.

*Teacher should time and direct each part. Time for 6 seconds, then multiply by 10.

Pulse Rate	Sitting	Walking Around Room for 1 Minute	Wait 2 Minutes, Then Standing	After 25 Jumping Jacks	Wait 1 Minute, Then Lying Down	After Jogging in Place for 2 Minutes	After Resting for 5 Minutes
in 6 seconds							
in 1 minute							

You should have found that your heart beats faster when you are active. That's because your body uses more oxygen when it exercises, and the blood must circulate faster to get more oxygen! Now, in a group of four, compare pulse rates and find the average for your group (using the 1 minute rate).

Pulse Rate	Sitting	After Walking	After Standing	After Jumping	After Lying Down	After Jogging	After Resting
You							
Person #2							
Person #3							
Person #4							
Total							
÷ 4 to find average							

Build a Blood Cell!

Our blood is made of millions of very tiny pieces called cells. There are red blood cells, white blood cells and cells called platelets. They are all so tiny that about 100,000 of them could fit on the head of a pin!

The job of red blood cells is to carry oxygen from the lungs to the body's tissues. White blood cells protect the body from disease. Platelets help prevent bleeding from damaged blood vessels. Each blood cell has its own parts. Look at the picture below and study the parts of the red blood cells. Remember, this is much bigger than a real cell.

Make a blood cell following these directions:

Materials Needed

1 plastic bag that seals
1 dark button
1/2 cup red Jell-O™ (made)

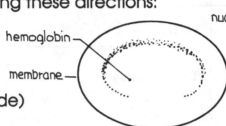

Red blood cell
(erythrocytes)

White blood cell
(lymphocyte)

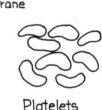

Platelets

Directions

1. Put the Jell-O™ in the bag.
2. Place the button in the bag.
3. Zip it closed tightly.
4. Squeeze the button to the center of the bag.

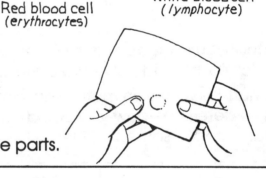

Draw your red blood cell and label the parts.

*Did you know that if your blood vessels were laid end to end, they would encircle the globe two and a half times?

Ingenious Genes

Your body is made up of several tiny cells. In each cell, there are long strings called genes, which you inherited from your mother and your father. Your genes have much to do with the way you look. This is why we often look like our parents. Do you? Below is a table showing characteristics of a mother and father. See if you can find all of the possible combinations for their children. There are 16 possibilities!

	hair	eyes	skin	height
Mom	blonde	green	dark	short
Dad	red	blue	fair	tall

Example:
blonde hair
green eyes
dark skin
short

blonde hair
blue eyes
dark skin
short

It is not definite that you will look exactly like your mother or father. Some genes are stronger, or dominant, and some are carried down through generations.

Complete the chart for your own mother and father. Then, find all of the combinations that determine how you could have looked! (You may have fewer than 16 if any traits are the same.)

	hair	eyes	skin	height
Your Mom				
Your Dad				

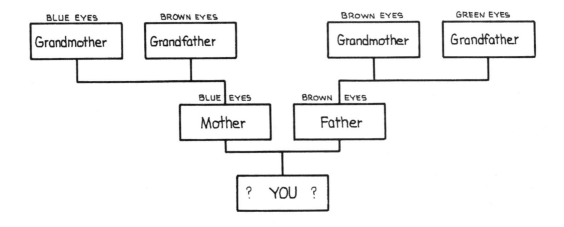

Name _____

Our Busy Brains

Your body's central nervous system includes your brain, spinal cord and the nerves coming out of these organs. It is responsible for receiving information from your senses, analyzing this information and deciding how your body should respond. Once it has decided, it sends instructions triggering the required actions.

The central nervous system makes some simple decisions about your body's actions within the spinal cord. These are called spinal reflexes and include actions like pulling your hand away from a hot object. For the most part, however, the majority of decisions involve the brain.

Your brain controls almost all of the activities in your body, but it weighs about 3 pounds. It is made up of three major parts - the cerebrum, the cerebellum and the brain stem. The cerebrum is divided into two hemispheres which are responsible for all thought and learning processes. The cerebellum is also divided into two parts, and they control all voluntary muscle movement. The brain stem which is about the size of your thumb, takes care of all involuntary functions. Look around your classroom. Everyone's brain is telling him/her to do things. Complete the list of jobs for each part of the brain below:

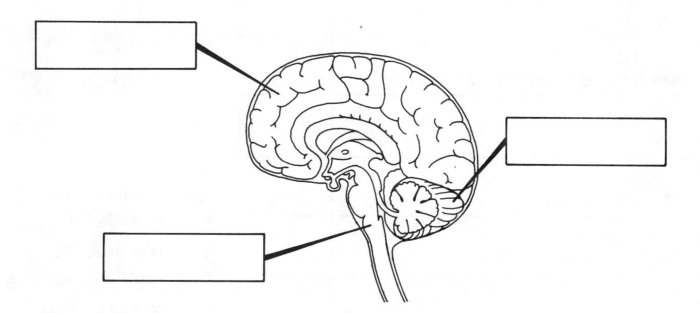

Name someone in your room who is using his/her cerebellum. _____

What is he/she doing? _____

Name someone who is using his/her brain stem. _____

What is he/she doing? _____

Name someone in your room who is using his/her cerebrum. _____

What is he/she doing? _____

Name _____

Find Your Brain Dominance

The two sides of the cerebellum work to control all voluntary movements. These include walking, running, writing and all other movements that we consciously want to do. One side of the cerebellum is usually dominant, or depended upon more heavily. The side that is dominant depends on the person. The left side of the brain controls the right side of your body and vice versa. That means that if a person writes with his/her right hand, he/she is probably left-brain dominant. Answer these questions to find your dominance.

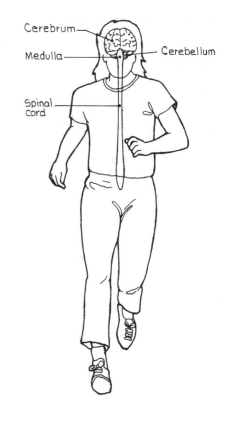

Try This:	Right	Left
Clasp your hands together. Which is on top?		
Pick up a pencil to write. Which hand do you use?		
Take 3 steps. Which foot did your start with?		
Try to do the splits. Which leg is in front?		
Hold your arms. Which arm is on top?		
Blink your eye. Which one did you wink?		
Pick up a fork. Which hand do you eat with?		
Hop 5 times on one foot. Which foot did you use?		
Look through a camera, telescope or microscope. Which eye did you use?		

How many times did you use your right? _____

How many times did you use your left? _____

Which side of your brain is probably more dominant? _____

(Be careful . . . they're opposite.)

*Make a class graph showing dominant sides.

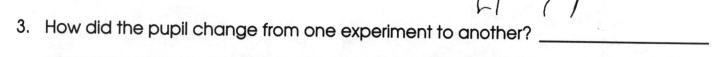

Name _____

Oh Yes, I See Now!

One of the most sensitive nerves in your body is the optic nerve. It is connected from your brain to the backs of each of your eyes. The optic nerve receives messages from other nerves that surround your eyes in the retina. As light is caught in the pupils of your eyes, it is first sent to the retina, then to the optic nerve and at last to the brain. Try this experiment to watch the pupil change!

1. Close your eyes and then cover them with your hands. Count to 100, open your eyes and immediately observe them in a mirror. Draw your eye below. Label the parts.

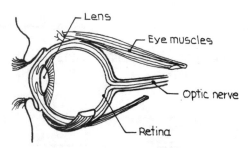

- Lens
- Eye muscles
- Optic nerve
- Retina

2. Now look at a light in your classroom. Count to 100 and draw your eyes. Label the parts.

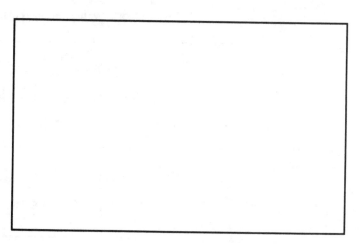

3. How did the pupil change from one experiment to another? _____

_____

4. Why do you think it changes? _____

_____

5. Why do people wear sunglasses? _____

_____

Name _____

Our Super Senses

The nervous system gets information about the world around us from sensory nerve cells. These nerve cells make up our five senses of sight, hearing, smell, taste and touch. Each of these senses plays a part in determining whether or not you like different foods. Try the experiments below and record your answers.

Look at the two gelatins in front of you.

Taste the red one. What flavor is it? _____

Taste the yellow. What flavor is it? _____

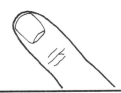

Gently touch the mashed fruit in front of you.

Now touch the sliced fruit. Taste each one.

Which tastes better to you? _____

Listen to your partner break some foods behind you.

Guess each food and record.

1. _____   2. _____

3. _____   4. _____

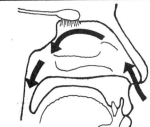

Gently sniff each envelope your partner holds under your nose.

Close your eyes and guess what each food is.

#1) 1. _____   2. _____   3. _____

#2) 1. _____   2. _____   3. _____

Your tongue has about 10,000 taste buds, each responsive to a different taste: sweet (sugar), sour (lemon juice), salty (salt), and bitter (cocoa). Use one end of a cotton swab for each different food and touch your tongue in different places.

Match these parts of your tongue with the taste they receive.

*Drink a sip of water between each food!

sides of tongue •   • bitter
tip of tongue •   • sweet
sides of tongue •   • sour
back of tongue •   • salty

My Body Homework

To keep your body working and looking its best, you should start good habits now and keep them as you grow older. Use this check list to keep yourself on track for the next week. Keep it on your bathroom mirror or next to your bed where it will remind you to do your "homework!"

	Sun.	Mon.	Tues.	Wed.	Thurs.	Fri.	Sat.
I slept at least 8 hours.							
I ate a healthy breakfast.							
I brushed my teeth this morning.							
I ate a healthy lunch.							
I washed my hands after using the bathroom.							
I exercised at least 30 minutes today.							
I drank at least 6 glasses of water.							
I stood and sat up straight.							
I ate a healthy dinner.							
I bathed.							
I brushed my teeth this evening.							

Your Pizza's Path

The digestive system is the group of organs that work together to gain fuel from the foods we eat and discard the unwanted waste. This system breaks down food into simple substances your body's cells can use. It then absorbs these substances into the bloodstream and any leftover waste matter is eliminated.

When you eat pizza (or any food), each bite you take goes through a path in the human body called the alimentary canal, or the digestive tract. This canal consists of the mouth, esophagus, stomach, and small and large intestines. It is in this path that foods are broken down, vitamins are saved and poisons are discarded. Study the path below.

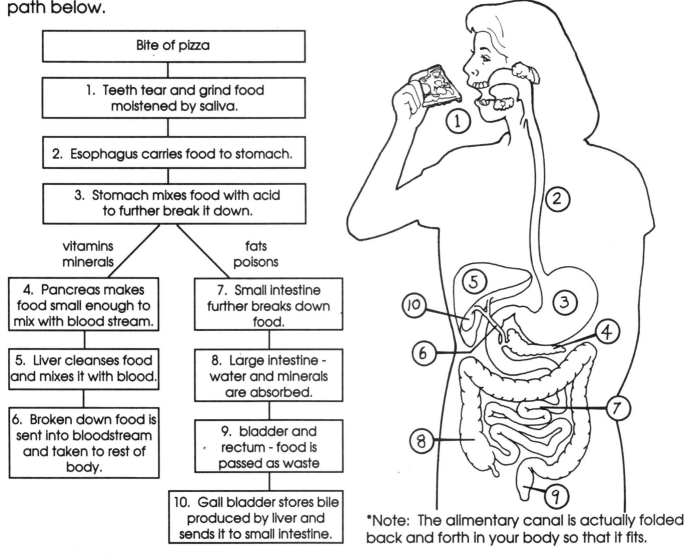

Bite of pizza

1. Teeth tear and grind food moistened by saliva.

2. Esophagus carries food to stomach.

3. Stomach mixes food with acid to further break it down.

vitamins minerals / fats poisons

4. Pancreas makes food small enough to mix with blood stream.

5. Liver cleanses food and mixes it with blood.

6. Broken down food is sent into bloodstream and taken to rest of body.

7. Small intestine further breaks down food.

8. Large intestine - water and minerals are absorbed.

9. bladder and rectum - food is passed as waste

10. Gall bladder stores bile produced by liver and sends it to small intestine.

*Note: The alimentary canal is actually folded back and forth in your body so that it fits.

1. Use a black crayon to trace the path of the healthy parts of the pizza.
2. Use a blue crayon to trace the path of the unhealthy parts of the pizza.
3. Name 3 parts of the pizza that are healthy. _____
4. Name 3 parts of the pizza that are unhealthy. _____

34

Which Path Will It Take?

In the story, *Bad Habit Harry*, most of Harry's food was filled with fat. Try this fat test to find fat in other foods.

Materials Needed

6" x 6" pieces of brown paper bags (one per student)
6 containers each containing 1/4 cup of the following:
    water, oil, peanut butter, soft cheese,
    orange juice, soft margarine
6 toothpicks (one in each container)

Directions

• Predict which foods contain fat on the chart below.
• Use the toothpick from each container to make a spot on your bag. Be careful to use small amounts so they won't run together.
• Wait several minutes and check the spots. Those with fat will leave a greasy spot.
• Record your observations.

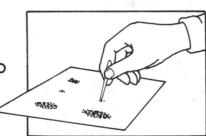

Name of Food	I Predict . . .		I Observed . . .	
	Fat	No Fat	Fat	No Fat

Which food seemed to have the most fat? Why?_____
Which food surprised you? _____
Which of the foods do you eat often? _____
What could you eat instead of the fatty foods? _____
On the back of this page, draw the path of these foods through the digestive system.

Art Projects

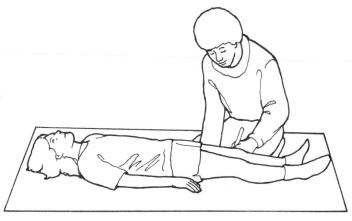

Build a Body

Students pair off and trace each other's bodies on butcher paper. Then, have them use yarn, balloons, paper towel tubes, fabric, buttons, etc. to create veins, organs, etc. Glue or staple them to the bodies and hang for display.

Advertise Good Health

Students can create and display posters about their bodies' systems and the importance of good health. Hang them around your school to spread the word.

Fool a Friend

Using plaster of Paris, children can create fake casts. Cover the forearm with an empty plastic bread bag. Cover only the top of the arm with plaster of Paris. Gently remove the bag and set the "cast" over jars lying on their sides. Allow it to dry for 24 hours. Have friends sign the cast and wear it home.

Inside Out!

Materials Needed: 1 T-shirt per student
paint pens or fabric paint
newspaper

Students decorate the front of the T-shirts to show the digestive system. On the back, paint part of the skeletal (ribs), circulatory (heart, veins, arteries), and nervous (spinal cord) systems. *Wear the T-shirts with shower caps explained below.

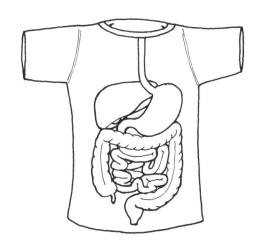

Brain Business

Line a bulletin board with white paper. Make mock brain waves going across the board. Cut a large brain out of grey construction paper. Put it in the center of the board. Title the board **Brain Business**. Have students write an incoming message to the brain on a strip of

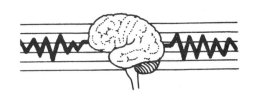

pink paper. Have them write an outgoing response on a yellow strip. Put the pink strip to the left of the brain and the yellow strip to the right. Connect the two with a black piece of yarn across the brain. Use straight pins to make the yarn look like brain waves.

More Art Projects

Picture Perfect

Divide the class into two teams. Gather and sit in teams in front of the chalkboard. One player from Team One picks a card, then draws a picture to describe the human body word on the card. Only his/her team may guess what the word is by shouting out answers. After one minute, if Team One hasn't guessed the correct word, Team Two may make one guess. If they don't guess the word, the point goes to Team One. Then Team Two picks a card and repeats the same procedure.

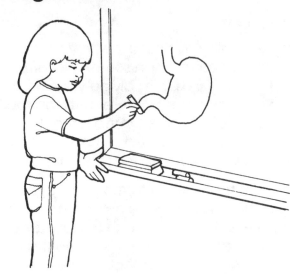

Some words to include are:
stomach, joint, cerebrum, vein, artery, pulse, lungs, blood cell, spinal cord, medulla, liver, cerebellum, humerus, bones, vertebrae, pelvis, clavicle, large intestine, pancreas, esophagus

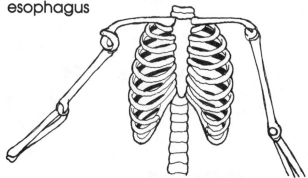

Construct a Skeleton

Students can work in groups to recreate a skeleton about 12" tall. Provide posterboard, construction paper, glue, markers and several pipe cleaners, etc. to each group and encourage them to cut, bend and twist the cleaners all they need.

Trap Textures in a Book

Feel different textures around the room. Look at a picture and describe the look of textures. Make texture books by clipping samples of different textures, or gluing a variety of materials or paper. For each page, use a different texture and write three sentences describing it. Example: fabric, grains of salt, oil, straw, cotton, etc.

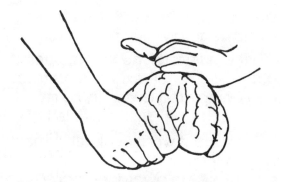

Models

As a homework assignment or whole class project, make models of the brain or sensory organs using clay, recyclable materials, Styrofoam, papier-mâché, etc.

Culmination of the Unit

Field Trips

- Make a visit to a hospital with your class. A teaching hospital can sometimes offer the best tours. If possible, divide your class into small groups so as not to disturb the routine of the hospital. Make certain the X-ray department is included in the tour. Ask for parent volunteers to accompany you.

- Science museums also make great field trips when studying the human body. If you are fortunate enough to have one in your area, schedule a field trip there. Most of them have a section devoted to the marvels of the human body.

Speakers

Have students write formal letters inviting members of the community (i.e. doctors, dentists, nurses, surgeons, nutritionists, athletes, coaches, etc.) to come speak to their class about good health and the human body.

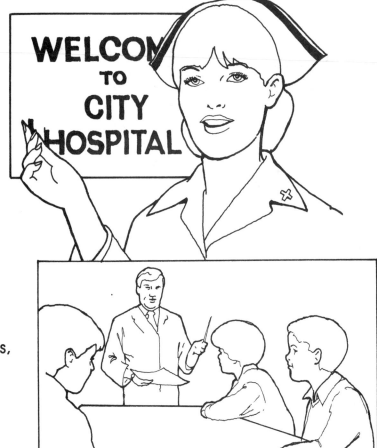

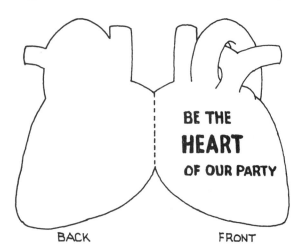

BE THE
HEART
OF OUR PARTY

BACK   FRONT

What We Learned About the Human Body

Fill in the final part of the K-W-L organizer. Let students tell you what they learned about the human body.

What Do I Think?

Give students copies of the Self Evaluation on page 43. Talk about what evaluation means. Go over each of the open-ended sentences and brainstorm the possibilities. Then, have the students fill them out. When they turn them in, give them one of the awards on page 48.

Healthy Human Body Bash

A great way to celebrate the completion of the unit on the human body is with a party.

Make invitations on different body parts (pages 40-42) and invite parents, grandparents, other classes and staff.

Serve healthy foods like fruits, vegetables and fruit and vegetable juices.

Share with the guests all the books, poems, art projects and science experiments that have been completed during the unit.

Dear Parents,

Today was the first day of our theme unit about **My Body**. We are all excited about the fun we are going to have learning across the curriculum about the human body and its systems of circulation, nerves, digestion and bones. Each day, ask your child what went on at school. Emphasize questions about the human body such as:

- Which organ pumps blood? (heart)
- What carries your blood? (veins and arteries)
- Which system pumps blood through your body? (circulatory)
- The brain is part of which of your body's systems? (central nervous)
- Your bones are part of which system? (skeletal)

We are creating a human body environment in our classroom. If you have any books or objects relating to this topic, we would appreciate your lending them to us, and we will take very good care of them. Please identify any articles you send so they can be returned to you. Also, if your job relates in any way to the human body, perhaps you would like to come share some information with our class. If you can help in any way, please check and return the form below.

Thank you for your continued support.

_____
Teacher

I can do one or more of the following:

☐ Read a book about the human body to the class

☐ Bring items related to the human body for display

☐ Bake body-shaped cookies for the Better Body Bash

☐ Come talk to the class about the human body
   Explain _____
   _____

☐ Help with food at the Better Body Bash

_____   _____
signed   date

Patterns

large intestine

esophagus

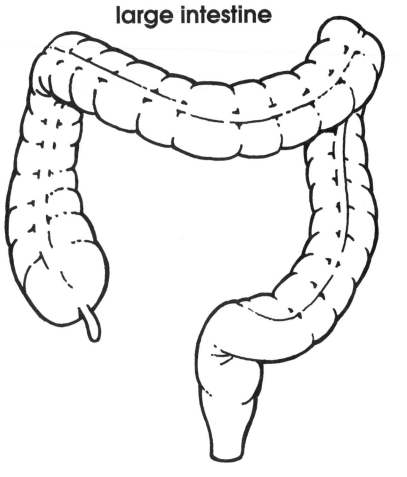

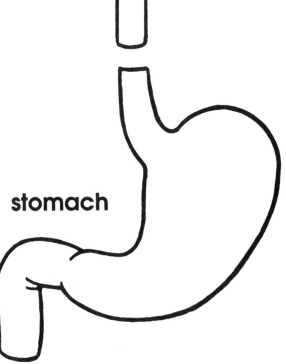

small intestine

stomach

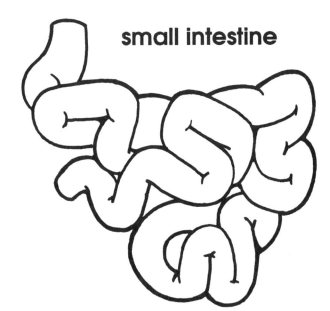

Patterns

brain

cerebrum

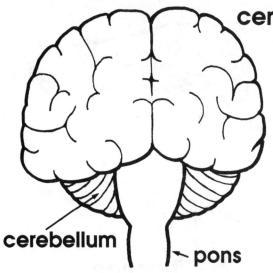

cerebellum — pons

Patterns are designed to fit on mural skeleton or can be reduced to fit on skeleton on page 44.

spinal cord

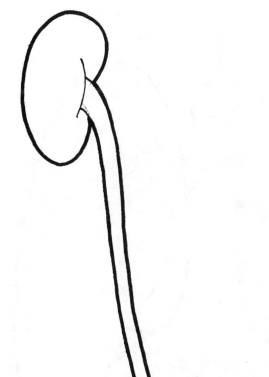

spleen

kidneys   bladder

Patterns

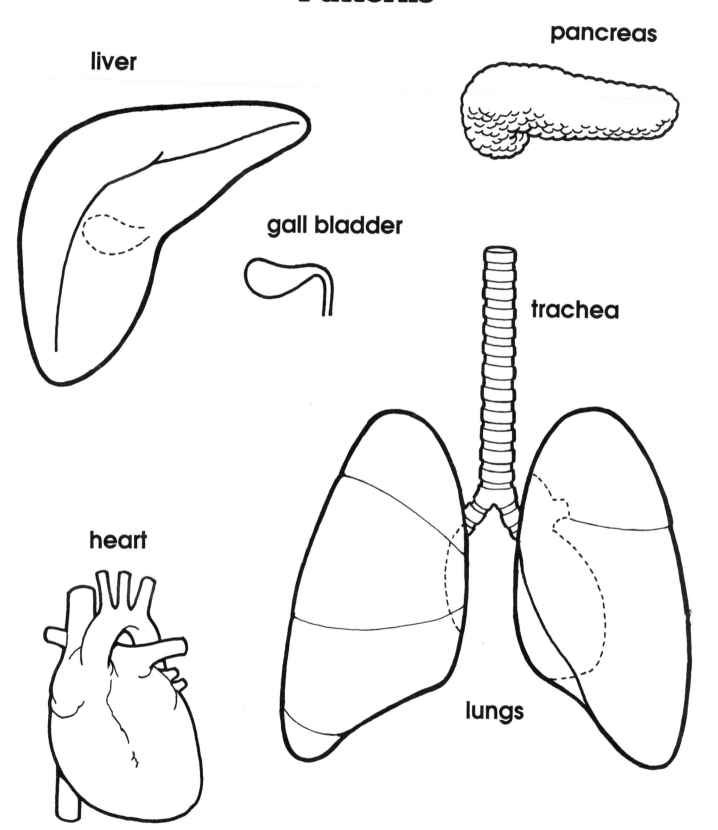

pancreas

liver

gall bladder

trachea

heart

lungs

Whole Language Evaluation
for My Body Theme Unit

Student's Name _____   Date _____

Self-Evaluation

I learned the following things about the human body _____
_____
_____

I made _____
_____
_____

The best piece of writing I did was _____
_____   because _____
_____

Of all the things I read, my favorite was _____
I liked it because _____
_____

The hardest part of the unit was _____
because _____
I helped the unit be a success because I _____
_____

My favorite activity was _____
because _____

Teacher Evaluation

Group participation _____
_____

Reading progress _____
_____

Writing progress (content area, creative writing, assigned writing) _____
_____

Oral Communication _____
_____

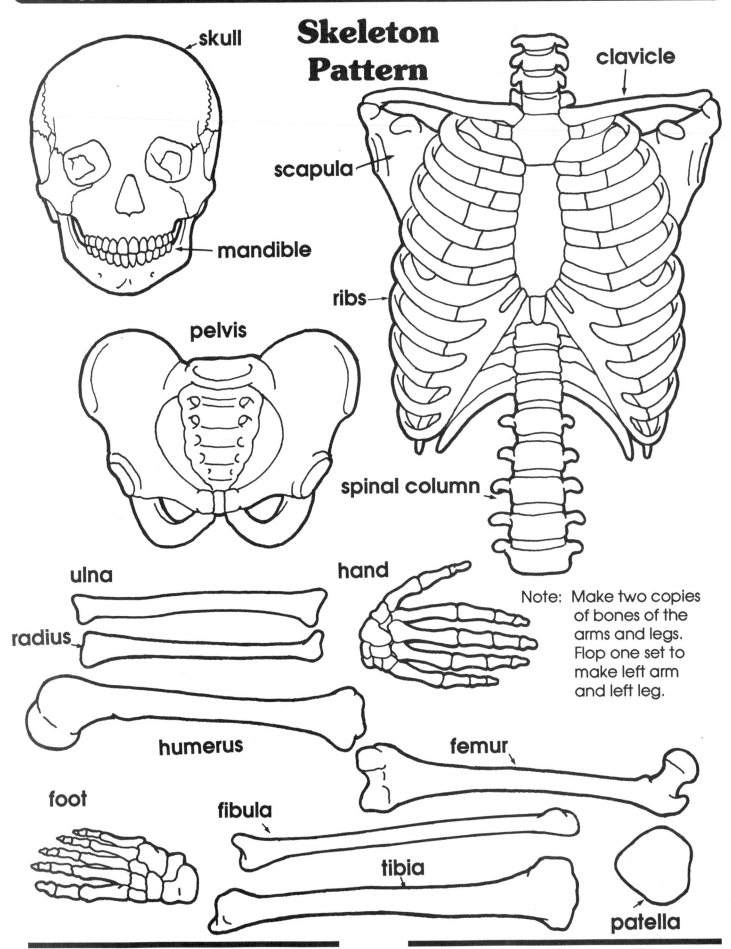

Skeleton Pattern

skull

clavicle

scapula

mandible

ribs

pelvis

spinal column

ulna

hand

radius

Note: Make two copies of bones of the arms and legs. Flop one set to make left arm and left leg.

humerus

femur

foot

fibula

tibia

patella

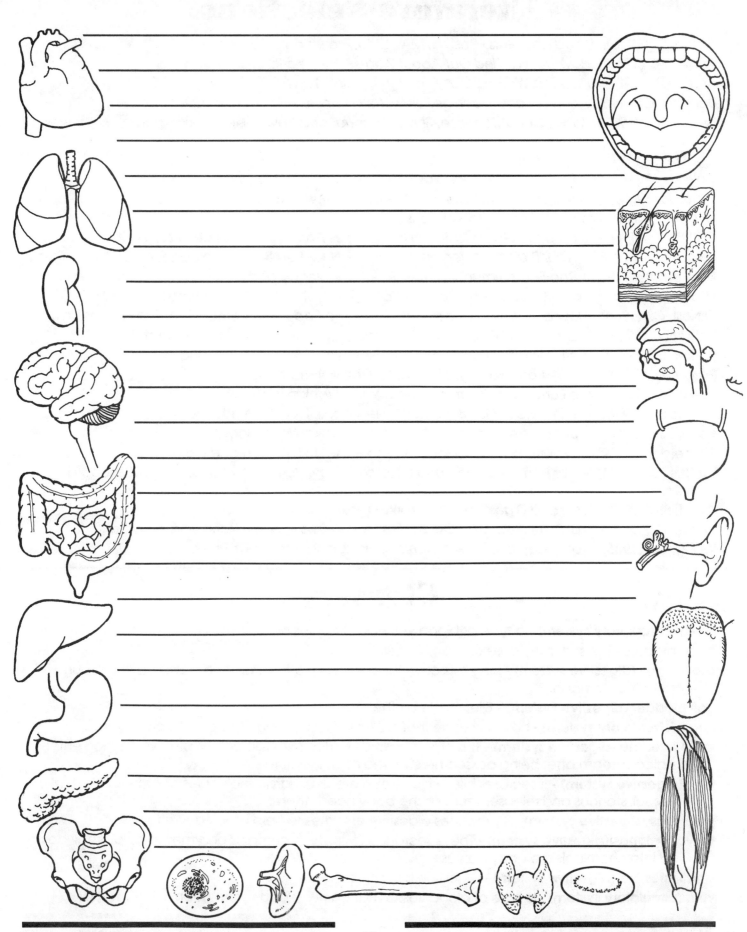

Literature Selections

Allison, L. (1976). *Blood and Guts.* Boston, MA: Little, Brown and Company.

Asimov, I. (1986). *How Did We Find Out About Blood?* New York: Walker and Co.

Asimov, I. (1987). *How Did We Find Out About the Brain?* New York: Walker and Co.

Barnard, C. (1983). *Junior Body Machine.* New York: Crown Publishers, Inc.

Berger, M. (1983). *Why I Cough, Sneeze, Shiver, Hiccup, and Yawn.* New York: Thomas Y. Crowell Co.

Cobb, V. (1981). *How to Really Fool Yourself.* New York: Lippincott.

Cole, J. (1987). *The Human Body.* New York: William Morrow & Co., Inc.

Cole, J. (1988). *The Magic School Bus Inside the Body.* New York: Scholastic, Inc.

Fryer, J. (1961). *We Hear.* Lerner Publications.

Griffith, H. (1986). *Complete Guide to Sports Injuries.* Los Angeles, CA: Price, Stern & Sloan, Inc.

LeMaster, L. (9184). *Your Brain and Nervous System (A New True Book).* Chicago, IL: Childrens Press.

McAleer, N. (1985). *The Body Almanac.* New York: Doubleday and Co., Inc.

Michaud, E., Anastas, L. (1988). *Listen to Your Body.* Pennsylvania: Rodale Press.

O'Neill, C. (1988). *How and Why - A Kid's Book About the Body.* Mt. Vernon, NY: Consumers Union.

Paige, D. (1985). *A Day in the Life of a Sports Therapist.* Mahwah, NY: Troll Associates.

Parker, S. (1990). *The Brain and Nervous System.* New York: Franklin Watts, Inc.

Parker, S. (1989). *The Eye and Seeing.* New York: Franklin Watts, Inc.

Parker, S. (1989). *The Lungs and Breathing.* New York: Franklin Watts, Inc.

Parker, S. (1989). *The Skeleton and Movement.* New York: Franklin Watts, Inc.

Parker, S. (1989). *Touch, Taste and Smell.* New York: Franklin Watts, Inc.

Schneider, T. (1976). *Everybody's a Winner.* Boston, MA: Little, Brown and Co.

Vevers, G. (1984). *Your Body: Feeding and Digestion.* New York: Lothrop, Lee & and Shepard Books.

Ward, B. (1982). *Food and Digestion.* New York: Franklin Watts, Inc.

Whitfield, P., Whitfield, R. (9188). *Why Our Bodies Stop Growing.* New York: Viking Kestrel.

Wong, O. (1986). *Your Body and How It Works.* Chicago, IL: Children's Press.

Glossary

artery (circulatory system) - a type of blood vessel that carries blood down from the heart

bone marrow - the soft, fatty core of many bones

esophagus (digestive system) - long muscular tube leading to the stomach; Food travels through here to the stomach.

gall bladder (digestive system) - Bile, made by the liver, is stored here.

heart (circulatory system) - hollow muscle that pumps blood through the circulatory system

large intestine (digestive system) - This organ absorbs water, minerals and waste, which then enter the bloodstream after being passed here by the small intestine.

liver (digestive system) - It secretes bile, which helps break up large molecules of fatty foods. It also stores substances and releases them as the body needs them.

pancreas (digestive system) - It produces digestive enzymes to help break down foods.

salivary glands (digestive system) - These secrete saliva which contains enzymes to help break down food into chemicals the body can use.

small intestine (digestive system) - Digestion is completed here.

vein (circulatory system) - a type of blood vessel that carries blood to the heart

The Human Body Gameboard

Gameboard

A good review of the study of the human body can be done through clues that are written about all systems of the body. Share with the students the gameboard on the back cover of the unit. You might want to laminate it first. You can work as a group to make up clues or use the ones below and add to them. The clues below reflect different areas of the curriculum.

Game Rules

Two to four children may play at one time. There should be an assigned reader who reads the clues and checks the answers, or the players may read the questions to each other. If the question is answered correctly, the person or group answering the question moves ahead one space. (Some of the harder questions may be given more value.) The students or groups keep taking turns until the first student or group reaches the United States. Ordinary buttons can be used as markers.

Game Cards

Find a body word in the dictionary. **Move 1 space.**	Name someone in your room using good posture. **Move 3 spaces.**	Name a disease and the part of the body it strikes. **Move 1 space.**	Sing a short song about your body. **Move 2 spaces.**
Name 4 organs that are part of the digestive system. **Move 2 spaces.**	Name 3 parts of the brain. **Move 3 spaces.**	Name 3 parts of the circulatory system. **Move 3 spaces.**	Name 3 types of doctors. **Move 3 spaces.**
Name 4 bones. **Move 2 spaces.**	Spell the name of one of your body's systems. **Move 1 space.**	How many bones are in an adult skeleton? **Move 3 spaces.**	What is calcium? **Move 1 space.**
Tell a joke about the body. **Move 3 spaces.**	Name a book about your body and the author. **Move 2 spaces.**	What is the measurement of your wrist in centimeters? **Move 1 space.**	Name three systems in your body. **Move 2 spaces.**

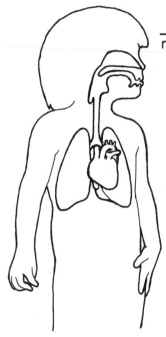

_____
name

has learned a

"healthy"

amount of knowledge
about the

HUMAN
BODY!

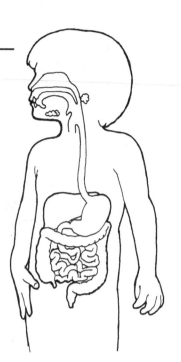

_____   _____
signature   date

Everybody
knows what a great job

_____
name

did in learning about the

HUMAN BODY!

Presented for: _____

_____

_____

_____   _____
signature   date